T0222014

O N E

I saw someone at the bookstore buying *One-Punch Man*. I couldn't help but stare. I'm not some kind of weirdo.

—ONE

Manga creator ONE began *One-Punch Man* as a webcomic, which quickly went viral, garnering over 10 million hits. In addition to *One-Punch Man*, ONE writes and draws the series *Mob Psycho 100* and *Makai no Ossan*.

Y U S U K E
M U R A T A
(AND THE CURRENT MEMBERS OF VILLAGE STUDIO)

The elite members of the studio continue to aim for new heights and polish their skills every day. If one looks like he's asleep, that's just your imagination.

—Yusuke Murata

A highly decorated and skilled artist best known for his work on *Eyeshield 21*. Yusuke Murata won the 122nd Hop Step Award (1995) for *Partner* and placed second in the 51st Akatsuka Award (1998) for *Samui Hanashi*.

ONE-PUNCH MAN | 04

ONE + YUSUKE MURATA

HEH

★ THE STORIES, CHARACTERS AND INCIDENTS MENTIONED IN THIS PUBLICATION ARE ENTIRELY FICTIONAL.

04

STORY BY
ONE

ART BY
YUSUKE MURATA

▶TANK-TOP TIGER

▶BANG

▶S·A·I·T·A·M·A

CHARACTERS

▶ GENOS

▶ SONIC

STRAW- BERRY SYRUP

STORY

A single man arose to face the evil threatening humankind!
His name was Saitama. He became a hero for fun.

Saitama went with Genos to take the professional hero exam and passed with
flying colors on his first try! Now he begins his service as a new Class-C hero.

But he wasn't aware of his quota of one heroic deed per week, so he is
suddenly faced with the crisis of losing his registration! As he races around
town looking for trouble, he runs into Speed-o'-Sound Sonic. Sonic wreaks
havoc on the city, and Saitama defeats him, but...

CONTENTS

ONE-PUNCH MAN VOLUME FOUR

ONE-PUNCH MAN
ONE + YUSUKE MURATA

My name is Saitama. I am a hero. My hobby is heroic exploits. I got too strong. And that makes me sad. I can defeat any enemy with one blow. I lost my hair. And I lost all feeling. I want to feel the rush of battle. I would like to meet an incredibly strong enemy. And I would like to defeat it with one blow. That's because I am One-Punch Man.

04

GIANT METEOR

HMM...

GENOS HAS A SUBSCRIPTION.
↓

SO IT WENT UP AFTER THAT FIGHT THE OTHER DAY?

RUSTLE

14 Tank
15 Metal
16 Puripur
7 Genos
ass-S Heroes

THAT IS WHY I AM RANK 17— THE BOTTOM OF CLASS S— IN THE ABILITY RANKING.

GULP

NO, NOT YET.

IT'S BEEN A WEEK. HAVE YOU DONE ANY HEROIC DEEDS?

WHY?!

SPURT

BUT IN THE WEEKLY POPULARITY RANKING VOTED ON BY CITIZENS, I AM NUMBER SIX.

"EXPECT MUCH FROM THIS GENIUS WHO DEBUTED IN CLASS S AT THE YOUNG AGE OF 19."

"A SENSE OF FRAGILITY UNDER THE STEELY EXPRESSION."

"HIS FACE IS GORGEOUS..."

"AMONG THE TOP FIVE BEST-LOOKING HEROES."

"HE'S THE CYBORG PRINCE."

"I LOVE THE COOL WAY HE REFUSES ALL MEDIA CONTACT."

RIGHT... OF COURSE...

THOSE COMMENTS WERE BASED MERELY ON MY PHOTO. THEY DO NOT REALLY KNOW ME, SO I DO NOT MIND.

AND SO ON.

DOESN'T IT EMBARRASS YOU TO READ ALL THAT?

I HAVE NEVER SEEN ANYONE AS INCREDIBLE AS YOU, MASTER, EVEN IF THE WORLD DOES NOT KNOW IT.

CUT THE FLATTERY. IT'S DISGUSTING.

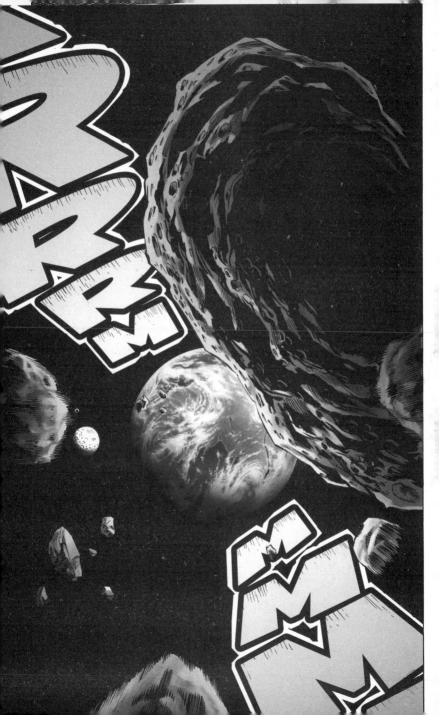

FOR SOME REASON, THE HERO ASSOCIATION IS SUMMONING ME.

I MUST GO.

MAYBE YOU'RE FIRED! HA HA!

OH!

Z city
BRANCH

...IS A CLASS-S, RANK-3 HERO.

...

BANG ...

HE POSSESSES TRUE SKILL.

I CAME BECAUSE THE ASSOCIATION CALLED ME.

T M P

THIS BRANCH OFFICE IS EMPTY.

EVERYONE IN THE ASSOCIATION HAS EVACUATED.

HWOOOOOOO

WE ARE THE ONLY TWO CLASS-S HEROES TO COME.

I SUPPOSE THE OTHERS WERE TOO FAR AWAY OR BUSY.

SOME PROBABLY JUST COULDN'T BE BOTHERED.

WHY DID THE OTHERS NOT COME?

THEY EVAC- UATED? WHY?

WHY DID THEY SUMMON ME?

THIS IS SURE TO BE MORE THAN WE CAN HANDLE.

SUMMONS ONLY GO OUT FOR THE BIGGEST, MOST IMPOSSIBLE TASKS.

THE ASSOCIATION WANTS NEARBY CLASS-S HEROES TO DO SOMETHING ABOUT A GIANT METEOR DUE TO HIT CITY Z IN 35 MINUTES.

IF IT STRIKES, IT WILL DESTROY THE CITY.

...THE HERO ASSOCIATION'S STATUS WILL RISE AND DONATIONS WILL POUR IN.

IF WE SUCCESSFULLY STOP IT...

I SUPPOSE *THAT'S* WHAT THEY'RE AFTER.

BUT IT'S IMPOSSIBLE.

A METEOR ?!

DOES THE POPULACE KNOW?

THIS TIME, THE PROBLEM'S TOO BIG.

YOU SHOULD FLEE WITH THOSE YOU CARE ABOUT.

...SO THE FIRST REPORTS MUST BE GOING OUT ABOUT NOW.

THEIR PLAN WAS TO ISSUE AN EVACUATION WARNING TO THE IMPACT AREA THIRTY MINUTES BEFOREHAND...

HA HA! IT'LL BE MASS PANIC!

GRIN

...A WARNING!

...HAS ISSUED...

THE HERO ASSOCIATION HAS ISSUED...

WARNING...

WHAT WILL YOU DO, OLD FELLOW?

ADDRESS ME AS MR. BANG.

Z CITY BRANCH....

HERO A

AH...

There it is...

...

RUN AS QUICKLY AND AS FAR AS YOU CAN!

I WANTED A GIRLFRIEND BEFORE I DIED...

WOOOOOOO

IT'S HUGE...

WE'RE DOOMED...

MANY ARE GIVING UP ON SURVIVAL.

THE SUR-ROUNDING TOWNS WILL ALSO BE DESTROYED!

THIS IS ABOUT MORE THAN CITY Z...

AND IT IS TOO LATE TO EVACUATE!

CLIK

TCH!

BEEP

ARMS MODE

IT IS TIME TO TEST THIS PROTOTYPE...

THIS CLASS-S, RANK-7 HERO USES MASSIVE FIREPOWER TO DEMOLISH HIS ENEMIES—ALONG WITH ANY BUILDINGS IN THE VICINITY!

DOES HE LIVE IN CITY Z TOO? OR HAS HE RISKED HIS LIFE TO COME HERE?

Y-YOU...

YES.

BOFOI. WORK TOGETHER WITH ME.

ARE YOU THE NEW HERO GENOS?

HAVE YOU COME TO STOP THE METEOR?

NO.

TEST? THIS IS NOT THE TIME.

WHY NOT?

IF THE METEOR STRIKES, YOU WILL DIE.

NO, I WILL NOT.

I MERELY CAME TO TEST A NEW WEAPON.

WHAT?

THE METEOR IS A CONVENIENT TARGET.

CALL ME *THE METAL KNIGHT.*

HEROES ADDRESS EACH OTHER BY THEIR HERO NAMES. THAT IS COMMON SENSE.

AND DO NOT CALL ME BOFOI.

TCH!

!

RRMMM

BUT...

...THERE IS NO MORE TIME FOR TALK.

WHSH

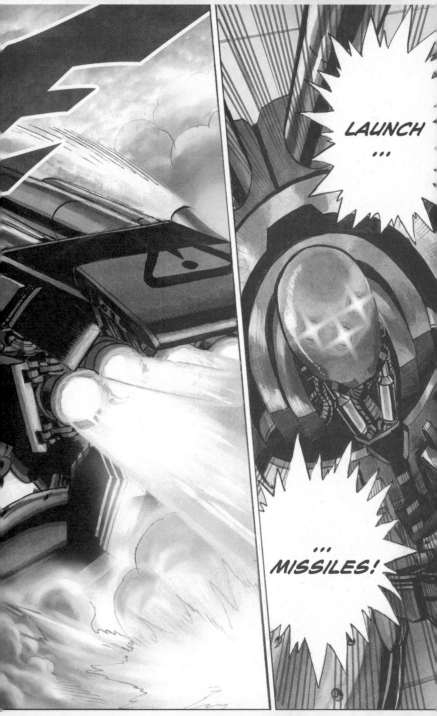

44

HE IS A DANGEROUS MAN!!

I MUST BE CAREFUL!!

...SUCH DESTRUCTIVE WEAPONS!

HE POSSESSES...

BO

OSH

?!

YOU ARE TOO YOUNG TO WORRY ABOUT FAILURE.

I CAN SEE YOU ARE UNSETTLED.

THE OUTCOME WON'T CHANGE, SO THAT'S BEST.

IN A PINCH, JUST MUDDLE THROUGH.

...IS BEST?

MUDDLING THROUGH...

WILL THIS PLACE...

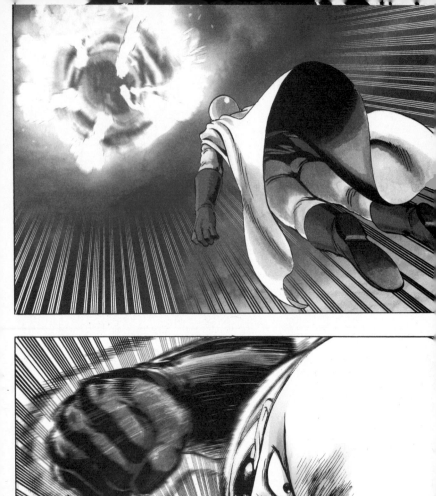

THIS IS *MY* TOWN ...

IF THE HERO ASSOCIATION HAD ASKED YOU INSTEAD OF ME FOR HELP...

...YOU AND THE METAL KNIGHT COULD HAVE COOPERATED TO KEEP THE DAMAGE TO A MINIMUM.

DON'T FRET OVER IT.

HE COULDN'T HAVE TEAMED UP WITH ANYBODY.

BUT THAT GUY WAS ONLY LOOKING OUT FOR HIMSELF.

NO ONE DIED, DID THEY?

I *DID* KEEP THE DAMAGE DOWN.

HE IS RIGHT.

ONE PUNCH FROM MASTER DECREASED THE METEOR'S FORCE AND LESSENED THE SHOCK WAVE.

OTHERWISE, EVEN IF PEOPLE HAD HIDDEN IN EVACUATION SHELTERS OR FLED TO THE SUBURBS, THE METEOR'S SHOCK WAVE WOULD HAVE BLOWN EVERYTHING AWAY.

IN TIME, CITY Z WILL RECOVER AND THE COMPLAINTS WILL CEASE.

I MUST NOT TELL HIM.

OUR RANKINGS WENT UP, RIGHT?

I ALMOST FORGOT.

SORCH SORCH

FAMP

YOU MOVED FROM CLASS C, RANK 342 TO RANK 5.

I MOVED FROM CLASS S, RANK 17 TO RANK 16.

HUH? OH... YES.

THE METAL KNIGHT WENT FROM CLASS S, RANK 7 TO RANK 6.

FROM 342 TO 5?! WHAT THE-?! ISN'T THAT WEIRD?!

...BECAUSE THE THREAT LEVEL WAS *DRAGON*.

NO. EVEN MOVING FROM CLASS A TO CLASS S WOULD HAVE BEEN UNDER-STANDABLE...

SIMPLY DESTROYING THE METEOR SHOULD HAVE LANDED YOU IN CLASS A, BUT THE HERO ASSOCIATION HAS ASSUMED THAT THE METAL KNIGHT AND I PLAYED AN IMPORTANT ROLE.

...Z...Z...

HUH...?

HAD YOU ALSO PREVENTED DAMAGE FROM THE DEBRIS, YOU WOULD HAVE JUMPED TO ABOUT CLASS S, RANK 5.

DOES THAT MEAN SOMETHING?

THE MEDIA ALWAYS TALKS ABOUT THREAT LEVELS LIKE DEMON AND TIGER.

Threat Level

God: A crisis threatening the extinction of humankind.

Dragon: A crisis threatening destruction of multiple towns.

Demon: A crisis threatening to interrupt a town's functioning or destroy it altogether.

Tiger: A crisis threatening massive loss of life.

Wolf: Appearance of a life-form or group posing a risk.

BUT MY OLD LANDLORD'S BUILDING IS FINE? TCH!

AGH! THE SUPERMARKET IS IN RUINS!

I'VE SEEN SOME DESTROYED TOWNS IN MY DAY...

THIS PLACE IS A WRECK...

...BUT IT SUCKS WHEN IT HAPPENS TO MY TOWN.

HUH?

HEY!

TUMP

WHAT'RE YOU DOIN' HERE...

...YOU *FRAUD.*

DON'T FORGET ME, YOU NEWB!

TANK-TOP TIGER!

UH... WHO ARE YOU?

I WON'T STAND FOR *LIES.*

BUT YOU SAY YOU PLAYED A BIG ROLE?

YOU'RE THE CLASS-C NOBODY WHO WORKED WITH CLASS-S HEROES TO DESTROY THE METEOR.

ARE YOU THE FRAUD WHO CLINGS TO CLASS-S HEROES AND STEALS THE CREDIT TO IMPROVE YOUR RANK?!

AREN'T YOU *ASHAMED*?! HUH?!

ONLY A *FAKE* COULD CLIMB THE RANKS SO FAST.

EVERYONE IN CLASS C HATES YOU!

HUH? GIMME A BREAK.

...WHAT DO YOU WANT?

SO, UH...

SOME GUYS ARE LIKE THIS.

HMM... I SEE...

IT'S *TIGER*! GRAH!

TANKTOP CIDER JUST MADE THAT UP.

WAIT, LI'L BRO.

YOU *KNOW* WHAT! WE'RE GONNA BEAT YOU INTO THE GROUND!

HA!

AND I KNOW THE *CRUELEST* WAY.

WE GOTTA DO WORSE THAN THAT.

HIS TYPE DON'T LEARN THAT WAY.

A H H H

HE'S RIGHT ...

...

LOOK AROUND! *YOU* DID THIS!

THEY TOOK THE BAIT !!!

THIS IS YOUR FAULT!

TH...

THOSE ARE THE *PAINED CRIES* OF THE *DISPLACED* !!

CAN YOU HEAR THAT ?!

110

SAITAMA
...

...YOU
SAVED
THIS
TOWN...

...BUT
THIS IS
HOW THEY
REACT.

GET
LOST!

GET
LOST!

GET
LOST!

THIS IS **REALITY.**

GET LOST!

GET LOST!

SO I WON'T SAY ANYTHING HERE.

QUITTING IS ONE POSSIBLE PATH.

YOU ARE PERHAPS THE STRONGEST I HAVE EVER ENCOUNTERED.

I DON'T WANT TO SEE YOU WASTE AWAY IN THIS PROFESSION!

HEY! HE JUST...

!

...MADE A SUS-PICIOUS MOVE!

NOW FOR THE FINISH!!!

I CAN'T *BELIEVE* YOU!

WHAT ARE YOU...

HUH?

...THE WAY YOU DESTROYED THIS *TOWN*?!

ARE YOU GOING TO *HURT* THESE PEOPLE...

THEY PLAN TO CRUSH THE NEW GUY...

...AS A PUBLICITY STUNT FOR THEMSELVES.

THOSE YOUNG ONES IN THE TANK TOPS ARE TOO GREEDY.

...AND NEVER MAKE IT PAST CLASS B.

I SHOULD GO.

THEY'LL FLAME OUT IN THE FINAL STRETCH...

YOU'RE A STAIN ON HEROES! SO WE'RE GONNA WIPE YOU AWAY!!!

GRAAAH!

TANK-TOP TIGER FIGHTS LIKE A TIGER...

...AND TANK-TOP BLACK HOLE HAS A CRUSHING, 200-KILO-GRAM GRIP!

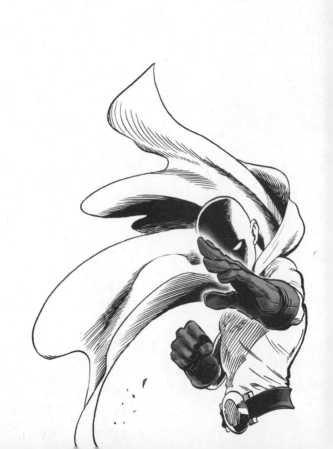

PUNCH 23: THREAT FROM THE SEA

RUM...BL...

MASTER, YOUR RANK HAS RISEN TO CLASS C, RANK 2.

THEN I WON'T HAVE TO DO ONE HEROIC DEED PER WEEK ANY-MORE.

SPSHS

CLASS B?

SOON YOU CAN ADVANCE TO CLASS B.

SPSHS

IF YOU REACH CLASS C, RANK 1, YOU CAN BECOME A B-RANKER ...

... BUT YOU COULD ALSO REMAIN AT CLASS C, RANK 1.

VWOO

CLINK

COR-RECT.

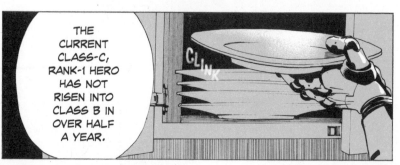

THE CURRENT CLASS-C, RANK-1 HERO HAS NOT RISEN INTO CLASS B IN OVER HALF A YEAR.

CLINK

RRING

THAT HERO...

EVEN WORSE IS THE CURRENT CLASS-B, RANK-1 HERO.

I SEE. UNDER-STOOD.

ARE NO CAPABLE HEROES NEARBY?

I MAY NOT ARRIVE IN TIME, BUT I WILL LEAVE NOW.

HE'S SO BUSY.

CITY J? THAT IS A LITTLE FAR...

PARDON ME.

HELLO?

SOME MONSTERS CLAIMING TO BE HIS CLAN MEMBERS ARE RAMPAGING IN CITY J.

A CLASS-A HERO IS HAVING TROUBLE FIGHTING THEM ALONE.

I DON'T REMEM-BER.

DID THAT MONSTER YOU DEFEATED LAST WEEK SAY HE WAS FROM THE CLAN OF THE SEAFOLK?

GENO

ARE THEY STRONG?

BIP

TROUBLE?

MONSTERS APPEAR AT CITY J SEASIDE!

THE CREATURES APPEARING IN CITY J CLAIM TO BE FROM THE CLAN OF THE SEAFOLK.

THEY ATTACK ANYONE THEY SEE. A HERO IS ATTEMPTING TO PREVENT THEIR ADVANCE...

THREAT LEVEL TIGER!!! CITIZENS, STAY AWAY!

...BUT HE MAY BE AT HIS LIMIT. HE LOOKS EXHAUSTED.

WE'LL HAVE TO HURRY.

SHALL WE GO?

QUA-DRUPLE THRUST!!

DID I JUST SINGLE-HANDEDLY BEAT A GOD-LEVEL INVASION?! I'M SO AW-W-W-WE-SOME!!

I DID IT... I DID IT!

CLASS-C HEROES

WE'RE TOO BACK-HEAVY!

HOW MANY ARE HITCHING A RIDE?!

I'M RARIN' TO GO!

WAIT UP, SEA PEOPLE!!

GO FASTER!

I'M GOING FULL THROTTLE!

VROOOM

HOW FAR IS IT TO CITY J?

IF WE DON'T HURRY, OTHER GUYS WILL STEAL THE GLORY!

ZOOOOOM

SUCCESS, HERE I COME!

CQ.HERO

I'M ALREADY FLOORING IT!

STEP ON IT!

VROOM

...

VROOOOM

PUNCH 24: DEEP SEA KING

←CITY J
15km

I'LL RETURN THE KILLING OF MY SOLDIERS 100 MILLION TIMES OVER!

I WON'T LET *ANY* OF YOU ESCAPE.

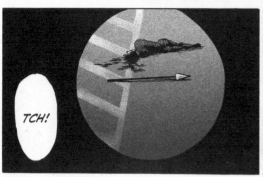

TCH!

...

IT LOOKS LIKE STINGER HAS PASSED OUT.

AM I TOO LATE?

BUT THERE'S ONLY ONE LEFT?

CHK

OR FACE HIM ONE-ON-ONE?

...

SHOULD I WAIT FOR BACKUP?

THAT HURT.

W...

WHAT THE HECK?!

WHAT'S THE BIG IDEA?

AND MY KICK PACKED WITH EXPLOSIVES DIDN'T WORK?

I WAS SO STARTLED I MADE A WEIRD SOUND!

HOW'D HE GET BEHIND ME?

UGH...

SHW

AM

I CAN'T FEEL ANYTHING... I CAN'T MOVE... AM I SAFE NOW?

I CAN'T BREATHE... AM I IN THE BUILDING ACROSS THE STREET?

NO, THAT'S... AN EARTH-QUAKE?

RRM

M M M M M

I' GOTTA GET OUT OF HERE...

ARGH...

THANKS.

?!

YOU'RE PRISONER 4188.

RRMM

I WAS DOING 10,000 YEARS FOR GETTING GRABBY WITH MEN!

MMMMMM

SUR- PRISED? I KEEP TABS ON GUYS WHO STRIKE MY FANCY.

YOU NEED TO BE LOCKED UP...

BONUS MANGA: PURISON

I'M SURPRISED A BRAND-NEW CLASS-C HERO...

...COULD BRING DOWN SUCH A NASTY ASSASSIN.

NNN

THE HOLDING CENTER HAD A HARD TIME.

HE ALWAYS SLIPPED OFF HIS CUFFS...

...AND ATTACKED HIS CELLMATES.

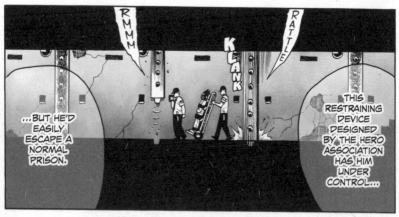

...BUT HE'D EASILY ESCAPE A NORMAL PRISON.

THIS RESTRAINING DEVICE DESIGNED BY THE HERO ASSOCIATION HAS HIM UNDER CONTROL...

BEYOND THIS DOOR...

WE'VE ARRIVED.

...IS
YOUR
NEW
HOME...

...SPEED-
O'-SOUND
SONIC.

The Stink Slammer ...

...is a prison for violent offenders who are difficult to handle.

WOOOOOOO

The inmates have monstrous strength sufficient to pry open iron bars with their bare hands.

Truly **uncommon** criminals lurk here.

Some require isolation to stop them from harming the mental well-being of others.

They can use everyday items to make keys, weapons or poisons.

HYUK HYUK HYUK!

ANOTHER SCRAWNY DUDE.

TUMP

TUMP

YOU GOT IT.

CLOMP

GO.

HEH... LET'S *PLAY.*

HMPH
...

LEMME SHOW YOU HOW IT'S DONE.

HE DISLOCATED MY SHOULDER!

YAOW!!

LOSER
...

WHAT'RE YOU IN FOR?

YO, NEW DUDE.

GUESS THAT'S WHY YER HERE.

YOU MAY BE KINDA TOUGH...

HEH.

YOU LOOK FEISTY.

ONE: NEW DUDES MUST ALWAYS OBEY OLDER—

...BUT LISTEN UP.

GET LOST.

WE GOT RULES HERE.

HUH?

...

GA HA HA! BEAT 'IM GOOD!!!

IDIOT. HE ANGERED DESTROYER JOHN.

I HEARD YOUR CHEEK-BONE SHATTER—

HAH HAH! I NEVER HOLD BACK!

THERE! BY THE WALL!!

SINCE WHEN?!

WHAT HAPPENED?!

HUH?! WHERE'D THAT DUDE GO?!

GYAOUCH!!

AND I CAME IN THROUGH MULTIPLE HEAVY DOORS...

A THICK STEEL WALL...

NO USE WORRYIN' OVER ESCAPE!

THINK ABOUT HOW TO SPEND YOUR LIFE HERE!

...AND NO WINDOWS.

I SEEN YOUNG GUYS LOSE THEIR *MARBLES* IN HERE!

IT'S MY ONLY ENTERTAINMENT!

NO SALVATION NEITHER! HEE HEE!

AIN'T GOT NO *MORALS* IN HERE!

JUST IMAGININ' IT GETS ME DROOLIN'! HEE HEE!

THAT PROUD FACE WILL CONTORT WHEN IT HITS BOTTOM!!

?

HEH HEH. IS IT ANY DIFFERENT OUTSIDE?

NO MORALS, HUH?

AND I GUESS EVEN VIOLENT CRIMINALS HAVE TO RESPECT EACH OTHER, OR COMMUNAL LIFE BREAKS DOWN.

IT'S ADMIRABLE FOR LOSERS TO CONGREGATE, CREATE THEIR OWN "ORDER" AND HOLD EACH OTHER UP.

...?

BUT I'M DIFFERENT.

IT'S ALL ABOUT WEAKNESS.

BY *KILLING* YOU ALL!

I'LL BE COMFORTABLE HERE. KNOW HOW?

W-WHY YOU ...!!!

?!

YOU WANT I SHOULD BREAK HIM?

WAIT. I'LL DO IT.

HE SEEMS CONFIDENT.

YOU WANNA CLIMB THE RANKS HERE? START WITH *ME*.

I'M THE ONLY ONE WHO'S EVER ROBBED A BANK BARE-HANDED!

I'M WARNING YOU. I USE KENPO.

G WOO OOO

BUT WHAT'S THE POINT IF YOU GET CAUGHT?

BW

HERE I COME!

GR-RA-A-A...

SH

194

SHH! BOSS WOKE UP!

QUIET... BE STILL!

WHAT'S THE MATTER?

YOUR ATTITUDE SUDDENLY CHANGED.

BOSS INSISTS...

...WE INMATES GET ALONG.

DON'T EVEN *THINK* ABOUT IT!

SO IF I BEAT HIM, THEN...

BOSS?

YOU SHOULDN'T HAVE YELLED!

PLEASE. JUST COOPERATE OR WE'LL *ALL* PAY.

THAT WAS UNTIL BOSS CAME!!

IT'S A LITTLE DIFFERENT NOW!

HOLD ON A SECOND...

WHAT WAS THAT ABOUT *MORALS*?

SORRY...

I WONDER WHAT HE'S LIKE?

THEY'RE SCARED TO DEATH OF HIM.

AS PUNISH-MENT LATER...

...I'LL DEEP KISS ALL OF THEM.

WERE THEY BULLYING THE NEW GUY?

#4188 SONIC

THOSE RASCALS...

FWIP

HE CAUGHT A MAN WITH AN A-CLASS BOUNTY ON HIS HEAD AND CAME HERE WITH HIM.

BOSS CAME ABOUT ONE YEAR AGO.

Former A-Class wanted man

HE'S A *SHELL* OF A MAN NOW.

WORD IS HE *WANTED* TO BE HERE.

...WAS EXACTLY HIS TYPE.

APPARENTLY THE GUY HE CAUGHT...

ATTACKING NORMAL GUYS IS WRONG...

BOSS REALIZED SOMETHING HERE.

I DON'T LIKE WHERE THIS IS GOING...

IF WE'RE GOOD, HE KISSES US ON THE CHEEK, BUT...

BOSS'S REACH IS LONG...

EVEN A CRUSTY VETERAN LIKE ME IS SCARED...

IS HE FRIENDS WITH THE GUARDS OR SOMETHING?

ONLY BOSS CAN GET OUT.

HEH! I KNEW THERE WAS A WAY!

YOU SAID HE BREAKS OUT?

EARLIER, YOU WAS TALKIN' ABOUT WEAKNESS.

YOU WOULDN'T SAY THAT IN FRONT OF BOSS.

A HERO IS ATTEMPTING TO PREVENT THEIR ADVANCE.

THE CREATURES APPEARING IN CITY J CLAIM TO BE FROM THE CLAN OF THE SEAFOLK.

THEY'RE GOING TO HURT STINGER !!!

OH NO !!

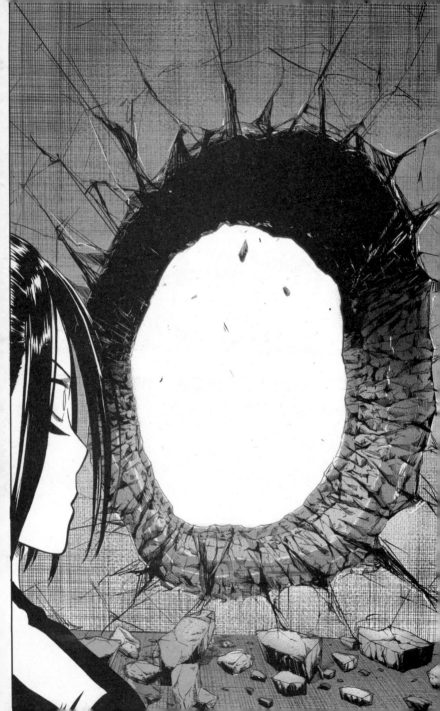

ONLY BOSS CAN MAKE A GETAWAY.

GUARDS WILL BE HERE IN FIVE SECONDS. STEP OUTSIDE AND YOU'RE SWISS CHEESE!

BOSS MADE ANOTHER HOLE.

SHOULD WE GO TOO?

WHO IS HE?

HE'S MORE POWERFUL THAN HAMMERHEAD'S SUIT!

WEEOOO

HE'S A CLASS-S HERO.

HE'S *PURI-PURI PRISONER.*

HM? WHERE'D THE NEW GUY GO?

4 Giant Meteor (End)

OH NO. THERE WAS A SALE YESTERDAY.

UH-OH!

THIS FLIER...

BONUS

WHAT A WASTE!

AW, MAN...

THE CREATURES APPEARING IN CITY J CLAIM TO BE FROM THE CLAN OF THE SEAFOLK.

Bonus (End)

END NOTES

PAGE 8, PANEL 1:
The back of Saitama's shirt says Chicago
and the front says Bulls.

PAGE 10, PANEL 1:
Saitama's bookshelf contains ONE's book
Mob Psycho 100.

BA DUMP
BA DUMP

ONE-PUNCH MAN
VOLUME 4
SHONEN JUMP MANGA EDITION

STORY BY | ONE
ART BY | YUSUKE MURATA

TRANSLATION | JOHN WERRY
TOUCH-UP ART AND LETTERING | JAMES GAUBATZ
DESIGN | FAWN LAU
SHONEN JUMP SERIES EDITOR | JOHN BAE
GRAPHIC NOVEL EDITOR | JENNIFER LEBLANC

ONE-PUNCH MAN © 2012 by ONE, Yusuke Murata
All rights reserved.
First published in Japan in 2012 by SHUEISHA Inc., Tokyo.
English translation rights arranged by SHUEISHA Inc.

The stories, characters and incidents mentioned in this
publication are entirely fictional.

No portion of this book may be reproduced or transmitted in any form
or by any means without written permission from the copyright holders.

Printed in the U.S.A.

Published by VIZ Media, LLC
P.O. Box 77010
San Francisco, CA 94107

10 9 8 7 6
First printing, January 2016
Sixth printing, July 2023

VIZ MEDIA
viz.com

SHONEN JUMP

RATED
TEEN
ratings.viz.com

PARENTAL ADVISORY
ONE-PUNCH MAN is rated T for Teen and
is recommended for ages 13 and up. This
volume contains realistic and fantasy violence.

★EYESHIELD 21

STORY BY RIICHIRO INAGAKI
ART BY YUSUKE MURATA

From the artist of *One-Punch Man!*

Wimpy Sena Kobayakawa has been running away from
bullies all his life. But when the football gear comes
on, things change—Sena's speed and uncanny ability
to elude big bullies just might give him what it takes to
become a great high school football hero! Catch all the
bone-crushing action and slapstick comedy of Japan's
hottest football manga!

VIZ media
www.viz.com

SHONEN JUMP
ADVANCED
www.shonenjump.com

RATED
T+
FOR OLDER
TEEN
ratings.viz.com

EYESHIELD 21 © 2002 by Riichiro Inagaki, Yusuke Murata/SHUEISHA Inc.

A KILLER COMEDY FROM *WEEKLY SHONEN JUMP*

A S S A S S I N A T I O N
CLASSROOM

STORY AND ART BY
YUSEI MATSUI

Ever caught yourself screaming, "I could just kill that teacher"? What would it take to justify such antisocial behavior and weeks of detention? Especially if he's the best teacher you've ever had? Giving you an "F" on a quiz? Mispronouncing your name during roll call...*again*? How about blowing up the moon and threatening to do the same to Mother Earth—unless you take him out first?! Plus a reward of a cool 100 million from the Ministry of Defense!

Okay, now that you're committed... How are you going to pull this off? What does your pathetic class of misfits have in their arsenal to combat Teach's alien technology, bizarre powers and...*tentacles*?!

ASSASSINATION
CLASSROOM

STORY AND ART BY
YUSEI MATSUI
1

SHONEN JUMP ADVANCED

Love triangle!
Comedic antics!!
Gang warfare?!

A laugh-out-loud story
that features a fake love
relationship between two
heirs of rival gangs!

Story and Art by
NAOSHI KOMI

NISEKOI
False Love

It's hate at first sight...rather, a knee to the head at first
sight when **RAKU ICHIJO** meets **CHITOGE KIRISAKI**!
Unfortunately, Raku's gangster father arranges a false love
match with their rival's daughter, who just so happens to be
Chitoge! Raku's searching for his childhood sweetheart from
ten years ago, however, with a pendant around his neck as a
memento, but he can't even remember her name or face!

AVAILABLE NOW!

Hikaru no Go

Story by **YUMI HOTTA**
Art by **TAKESHI OBATA**

The breakthrough series by Takeshi Obata, the artist of *Death Note!*

Hikaru Shindo is like any sixth-grader in Japan: a pretty normal schoolboy with a penchant for antics. One day, he finds an old bloodstained Go board in his grandfather's attic. Trapped inside the Go board is Fujiwara-no-Sai, the ghost of an ancient Go master. In one fateful moment, Sai becomes a part of Hikaru's consciousness and together, through thick and thin, they make an unstoppable Go-playing team.

Will they be able to defeat Go players who have dedicated their lives to the game? And will Sai achieve the "Divine Move" so he'll finally be able to rest in peace? Find out in this *Shonen Jump* classic!

RATED
A
ALL AGES
ratings.viz.com

SHONEN JUMP
www.shonenjump.com

VIZ
MEDIA
www.viz.com

STOP!

YOU'RE READING THE WRONG WAY!

⭐ ONE-PUNCH MAN READS FROM RIGHT TO LEFT, STARTING IN THE UPPER-RIGHT CORNER. JAPANESE IS READ FROM RIGHT TO LEFT, MEANING THAT ACTION, SOUND EFFECTS, AND WORD-BALLOON ORDER ARE COMPLETELY REVERSED FROM ENGLISH ORDER.

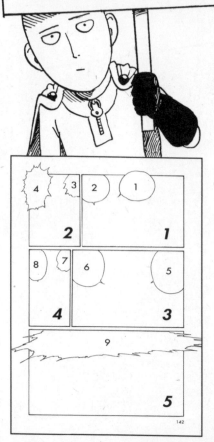